How Many Veggies?

by Phil Vischer

Tommy
NELSON

Thomas Nelson, Inc.
Nashville

Art Direction:
Ron Eddy

3D Illustrators:
Tom Danen, Robert Ellis,
Aaron Hartline, Adam Holmes,
Mike Laubach, Joe McFadden,
Daniel López Muñoz, Joe Sapulich,
Ron Smith and Lena Spoke

Render Management:
Jennifer Combs and Ken Greene

Published in Nashville, Tennessee, by Tommy Nelson™,
a division of Thomas Nelson, Inc.

Library of Congress Cataloging-in-Publication Data
Vischer, Phil.
    How Many Veggies? / by Phil Vischer.
      p. cm.
    Summary: Bob the Tomato is joined by nine other vegetables until
his boat becomes so full that it begins to sink.
    ISBN: 0-8499-1488-4, 0-8499-5985-3 (board), 0-8499-7674-X (mini),
0-8499-7578-6 (mini set)
      [1. Vegetables—Fiction. 2. Boats and boating—Fiction
3. Counting. 4. Stories in rhyme.] I. Title.
PZ8.3.V74Ho 1997
[E]—dc21

                                97-23986
                                  CIP
                                  AC

Printed in the United States of America

00 01 02 03 WCV 9 8 7 6 5 4 3 2 1

Dear Parent

We believe that children are a
gift from God and that helping
them learn and grow is nothing less
than a divine privilege.

With that in mind, we hope these
"Veggiecational" books provide years
of rocking chair fun as they teach
your kids fundamental concepts
about the world God made.

- *Phil Vischer*
President
Big Idea Productions

Bob the Tomato is taking a trip.
A day on the sea will be fun!
How many veggies are on his small ship?

The answer, of course, is 1!

Larry the Cucumber joins Captain Bob.
Could *he* find a place on the crew?
Maybe first mate — he'd be great for the job!

Now on the boat, there are **2**!

Two little veggies are taking a trip.
Junior says, "What about me?
I've got some crackers and soda to sip!"

Count them again, 1 – 2 – 3 !

Larry says, "Hey! Who will push us along?
I'm not very good with an oar.
Let's call Mr. Nezzer, because he's so strong!"

Now on the boat, there are **4**!

Junior says, "Captain! Our numbers are growing!
Soon we'll be rowing, the wind will be blowing,
But tell me please, how will we know where
    we're going
If no one is sitting up there?
We need someone up in the air!"

The gourd they call Jerry is next to arrive.
His compass and spyglass would help them survive!
So, quickly they vote him shipmate number **5**!

And send him up high in the air —
To stare at the sea from his chair.

Five little veggies, no room for another,
The perfect vocational mix!
'Til Jerry says, "Boy, I sure do miss my brother."

And Jimmy becomes number 6!

"Six is enough!" Bob remarks to his men,
"At least it's not ten or eleven."
But Percy jumps in, and when Bob counts again —

1 – 2 – 3 – 4 – 5 – 6 – **7**!

"Only one thing that we're missing!" says Larry,
"A parrot! Now that would be great!"
Then Laura shows up with her pet parrot, Harry.

And now on the boat there are !

Eight little veggies and one silly parrot
(Who came, you'll remember, with Laura the Carrot).
"The weight, sir!" says Junior, "our boat cannot bear it!
We're headed for trouble, I think —
Our boat is beginning to sink!"

Yes, eight little veggies, all trying to bail!
Starting to argue and whine —
"I'm coming!" yells Archie, "and I've got a pail!"

He jumps in, making it **9**!

Nine little veggies, all wet to their knees,
Beginning to shiver and shake,
Turn to see something come out of the trees
That makes their hearts quiver and quake!

Goliath the giant — a big, bumpy pickle —
Runs down to the dock with a shout!

"I'm no good at sailing, but I just love bailing!
So I'm going to help you guys out!"